MAKING
RADICAL
DISCIPLES

STUDENT GUIDE

Making Radical Disciples

A training manual to facilitate training disciples in house churches, small groups, and discipleship groups, leading towards a church-planting movement.

By Daniel B. Lancaster, Ph.D.

Published by:

T4T Press

First Printing, 2011

Copyright 2011 by Daniel B. Lancaster

ISBN 978-0-9831387-1-6 printed

Library of Congress Cataloging-in-Publication Data

Lancaster, Daniel B.

Making Radical Disciples: A training manual to facilitate training disciples in house churches, small groups, and discipleship groups, leading towards a church-planting movement. / Daniel B. Lancaster.

Includes bibliographical references.

ISBN 978-0-9831387-1-6

1. Follow Jesus Training: Basic Discipleship–United States.

I. Title.

Contents

Training

Reference

1

Welcome

Welcome opens the training sessions or seminar by introducing the trainers and learners. Trainers introduce learners to eight pictures of Jesus as the following: Soldier, Seeker, Shepherd, Sower, Son, Holy One, Servant, and Steward–with matching hand motions. Because people learn by listening, seeing, and doing, Follow Jesus Training incorporates each of these learning styles in every session.

The Bible says the Holy Spirit is our teacher; learners are encouraged to depend on the Spirit throughout the training. The session ends by opening a "tea shop" to provide a more relaxed atmosphere among trainers and learners, the kind of setting the disciples enjoyed with Jesus.

WORSHIP

BEGINNING

Who are the Trainers?

Who are the Learners?

Who is Jesus?

EIGHT PICTURES OF JESUS IN THE BIBLE

Soldier
Raise sword.

Seeker
Look back and forth with hand above eyes.

Shepherd
Move arms towards your body as if you are
gathering people.

Sower
Cast seeds with hands.

Son
Move hands towards mouth as if you are eating.

Holy One
Put hands in classic "praying hands" pose.

Servant
Wield a hammer.

Steward
Take money from shirt pocket or purse.

What are the Three Ways We Learn Best?

🖐 Listening

Cup your hand around your ear.

🖐 Seeing

Point to your eyes.

🖐 Doing

Make a rolling motion with your hands.

ENDING

The Tea Shop Is Open! ଦ୍ଧ

—Luke 7:31-35—Jesus went on to say: What are you people like? What kind of people are you? You are like children sitting in the market and shouting to each other, "We played the flute, but you would not dance! We sang a funeral song, but you would not cry!" John the Baptist did not go around eating and drinking, and you said, "John has a demon in him!" But because the Son of Man goes around eating and drinking, you say, "Jesus eats and drinks too much! He is even a friend of tax collectors and sinners." Yet Wisdom is shown to be right by what its followers do. (CEV)

2

Multiply

Multiply introduces Jesus as a Steward: stewards want a good return on their time and treasure, and they desire to live with integrity. Learners gain a vision for fruitfulness by exploring 1) God's first command to mankind, 2) Jesus' last command to mankind, 3) the 222 Principle, and 4) the differences between the Sea of Galilee and Dead Sea.

The lesson ends with an active-learning skit that demonstrates the difference in "yield", or fruit, between training others and merely teaching them. Learners are challenged to train people how to worship, pray, study God's word, and minister to others. With this investment of time, treasure, and integrity, learners will be able to give Jesus an amazing gift when they see Him in Heaven.

WORSHIP

PRAYER

STUDY

Review

What Are Eight Pictures That Help Us Follow Jesus?

Our Spiritual Life Is Like a Balloon

What is Jesus Like?

> *—Matthew 6:20-21—But store up for yourselves treasures in heaven, where moth and rust do not destroy, and where thieves do not break in and steal. For where your treasure is, there your heart will be also.*

Steward
 Pretend to take money from shirt pocket or purse.

What are Three Things a Steward Does?

—Matthew 25:14-28—For it is just like a man going on a journey. He called his own slaves and turned over his possessions to them. To one he gave five talents; to another, two; and to another, one—to each according to his own ability. Then he went on a journey. Immediately the man who had received five talents went, put them to work, and earned five more. In the same way, the man with two earned two more. But the man who had received one talent went off, dug a hole in the ground, and hid his master's money. After a long time the master of those slaves came and settled accounts with them. The man who had received five talents approached, presented five more talents, and said, "Master, you gave me five talents. Look, I've earned five more talents." His master said to him, "Well done, good and faithful slave! You were faithful over a few things; I will put you in charge of many things. Enter your master's joy!" Then the man with two talents also approached. He said, "Master, you gave me two talents. Look, I've earned two more talents." His master said to him, "Well done, good and faithful slave! You were faithful over a few things; I will put you in charge of many things. Enter your master's joy!" Then the man who had received one talent also approached and said, "Master, I know you. You're a difficult man, reaping where you haven't sown and gathering where you haven't scattered seed. So I was afraid and went off and hid your talent in the ground. Look, you have what is yours." But his master replied to him, "You evil, lazy slave! If you knew that I reap where I haven't sown and gather where I haven't scattered, then you should have deposited my money with the bankers. And when I returned I would have received my money back with interest. So take the talent from him and give it to the one who has 10 talents." (HCSB)

1. _____

2. _____

3. _____

What Was God's First Command to Man?

—Genesis 1:28—God blessed them; and God said to them, "Be fruitful and multiply, and fill the earth, and subdue it; and rule over the fish of the sea and over the birds of the sky and over every living thing that moves on the earth."(NASB)

_____

What Was Jesus' Last Command to Man?

—Mark 16:15—He said to them, "Go into all the world and preach the good news to all creation."

_____

How Can I Be Fruitful and Multiply?

—2 Timothy 2:2—The things which you have heard from me in the presence of many witnesses entrust these to faithful men who will be able to teach others also.(NASB)

Sea of Galilee/Dead Sea ❧

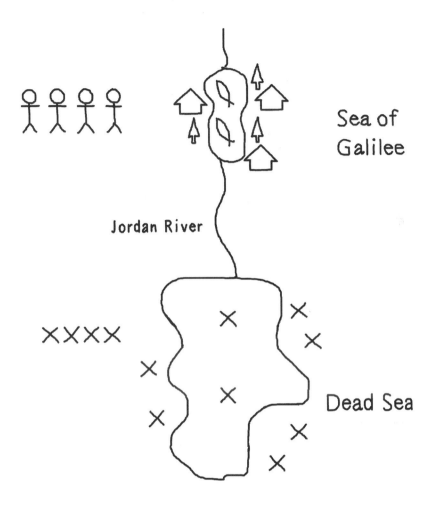

Jordan River

Sea of
Galilee

Dead Sea

Memory Verse

—John 15:8—This is to my Father's glory, that you bear much fruit, showing yourselves to be my disciples.

PRACTICE

"The *youngest* person in the pair will be the leader."

ENDING

"A Gift for Jesus" Skit ∝

Praise
Raise hands in worship to God.

Pray
Put hands in classic prayer pose.

Study the Bible
Put palms upward as if you are reading a book.

Tell others about Jesus
Put hand out as if you are spreading seeds.

3

Love

Love introduces Jesus as a Shepherd: shepherds lead, protect, and feed their sheep. We "feed" people when we teach them from God's Word, but what should be the first thing we teach people about God? Learners explore the most important commandment, identify who the source of love is, and discover how to worship based on the most important commandment.

Learners practice leading a simple disciple group with four key elements: worship (loving God with the whole heart), prayer (loving God with all the soul), Bible study (loving God with the all the mind), and practicing a skill (so we can love God with all our strength). A final skit, "Sheep and Tigers," demonstrates the need for many disciple groups among believers.

Worship

Prayer

1. How can we pray for lost people you know to be saved?
2. How can we pray for the group you are training?

- If a partner has not started training anyone, pray for potential people in their sphere of influence who they can begin to train.
- Partners pray together.

Study

Review

What Are Eight Pictures That Help Us Follow Jesus?

Multiply

What are three things a steward does?

What was God's first command to man?

What was Jesus' last command to man?

How can I be fruitful and multiply?

What are the names of the two seas located in Israel?

Why are they so different?

Which one do you want to be like?

What is Jesus Like?

—Mark 6:34—When Jesus went ashore, He saw a large crowd, and He felt compassion for them because they were like sheep without a shepherd; and He began to teach them many things. (NASB)

 Shepherd
Move hands towards your body as if you are
gathering people.

What are Three Things a Shepherd Does?

—Psalm 23:1-6—The LORD is my shepherd, I shall not want. He makes me lie down in green pastures; He leads me beside quiet waters. He restores my soul; He guides me in the paths of righteousness For His name's sake. Even though I walkthrough the valley of the shadow of death, I fear no evil, for You are with me; Your rod and Your staff, they comfort me. You prepare a table before me in the presence of my enemies; You have anointed my head with oil; my cup overflows. Surely goodness and loving-kindness will follow me all the days of my life, and I will dwell in the house of the LORD forever. (NASB)

1. _____

2. _____

3. _____

What is the Most Important Command to Teach Others?

—Mark 12:28-31—One of the teachers of the law came and heard them debating. Noticing that Jesus had given them a good answer, he asked him, "Of all the commandments, which is the most important?" "The most important one," answered Jesus, "is this: 'Hear, O Israel, the Lord our God, the Lord is one. Love the Lord your God with all your heart and with all your soul and with all your mind and with all your strength.' The second is this: 'Love your neighbor as yourself.' There is no commandment greater than these."

1. _____

✋ Put hands upwards towards God.

2. _____

✋ Put hands outwards towards others.

Where Does Love Come From?

—I John 4:7, 8—Dear friends, let us love one another, because love is from God, and everyone who loves has been born of God and knows God. The one who does not love does not know God, because God is love. (HCSB)

_____

18

Put hands upwards as if you are receiving loveand then give the love back to God.

Put hands upwards as if you are receiving love, then spread hands out as if you are giving it to others.

What is Simple Worship?

Praise
> Lift hands in praise to God.

Prayer
> Put hands in classic "praying hands" pose.

Study
> Put hands palms upward as if you are reading a book.

Practice
> Move hand back and forth as if you are casting seeds.

Why Do We Have Simple Worship?

–Mark 12:30–Love the Lord your God with all your heart, and with all your soul, and with all your mind, and with all your strength.

We...	So We...	Hand motions
Love God with all our Heart	Praise	✋ Put hand over heart and then raise hands up in praise to God.
Love God with all our Soul	Pray	✋ Clutch hands to sides and then put hands in classic prayer pose.
Love God with all our Mind	Study	✋ Put hand on the right side of the head as if thinking, and then put palms upward as if you are reading a book.
Love God with all our Strength	Share What We Have Learned	✋ Put arms up and flex muscles, then put hand out spreading seeds.

How Many People Does It Take to Have Simple Worship?

—Matthew 18:20—For where two or three come together in my name, there am I with them.

Memory Verse

—John 13:34, 35—So now I am giving you a new commandment: Love each other. Just as I have loved you, you should love each other. Your love for one another will prove to the world that you are my disciples. (NLT)

PRACTICE

"The *older person* in the pair will be the leader."

ENDING

Simple Worship

1. What does this story tell us about God?
2. What does this story tell us about people?
3. How will this story help me follow Jesus?

Why is it Important for You to Start a Disciple Group?

SHEEP AND TIGERS ❧

4

Pray

Pray introduces learners to Jesus as the Holy One. He lived a holy life and died for us on the cross. God commands us to be saints as we follow Jesus. A Saint worships God, lives a holy life, and prays for others. Following Jesus' example in prayer, we praise God, repent of our sins, ask God for the things we need, and yield to what He asks us to do.

God answers our prayers in one of four ways: no (if we ask with wrong motives), slow (if the timing is not right), grow (if we need to develop more maturity before He gives the answer), or go (when we pray according to His Word and will). Learners memorize God's phone number, 3-3-3, based on Jeremiah 33:3 and are encouraged to "call" God every day.

WORSHIP

.

PRAYER

1. How can we pray for lost people you know to be saved?
2. How can we pray for the group you are training?

STUDY

Telephone Game ∞

Review

What Are Eight Pictures That Help Us Follow Jesus?

Multiply

What are three things a steward does?

What was God's first command to man?

What was Jesus' last command to man?

How can I be fruitful and multiply?

What are the two seas located in Israel?

Why are they so different?

Which one do you want to be like?

Love

What are three things a shepherd does?

What is the most important command to teach others?

Where does love come from?

What is simple worship?

Why do we have simple worship?

How many people does it take to have simple worship?

What is Jesus Like?

–Luke 4:33-35–In the synagogue there was a man possessed by a demon, an evil spirit. He cried out at the top of his voice, "Ha! What do you want with us, Jesus of Nazareth? Have you come to destroy us? I know who you are–the Holy One of God!" "Be quiet!" Jesus said sternly. "Come out of him!" Then the demon threw the man down before them all and came out without injuring him.

"Jesus is the Holy One of God. He is the one we worship. He also intercedes for us before the throne of God. As Jesus' followers, we worship Him. He calls us to intercede on behalf of others and live a holy life connected to Him. Jesus is the Holy One. We are called to be saints."

 Put hands in classic "praying hands" pose

What are Three Things a Saint Does?

–Matthew 21:12-16–Jesus entered the temple area and drove out all who were buying and selling there. He overturned the tables of the money changers and the benches of those selling doves. "It is written," he said to them, "'My house will be called a house of prayer,' but you are making it a 'den of robbers.'" The blind and the lame came to him at the temple, and he healed them. But when the chief priests and the teachers of the law saw the wonderful things he did and the children shouting in the temple area, "Hosanna to the Son of David," they were indignant. "Do you hear what these children are saying?" they asked him. "Yes," replied

Jesus, "have you never read, 'From the lips of children and infants you have ordained praise'?"

1. _____

2. _____

3. _____

How Should We Pray?

—Luke 10:21—At that very time He rejoiced greatly in the Holy Spirit, and said, "I praise You, O Father, Lord of heaven and earth, that You have hidden these things from the wise and intelligent and have revealed them to infants. Yes, Father, for this way was well pleasing in Your sight." (NASB)

1. _____

✋ Hands raised in worship.

—Luke 18:13, 14—The tax collector stood off at a distance and did not think he was good enough even to look up toward heaven. He was so sorry for what he had done that he pounded his chest and prayed, "God, have pity on me! I am such a sinner." Then Jesus said, "When the two men went home, it was the tax collector and not the Pharisee who was pleasing to God. If you put yourself above others, you will be put down. But if you humble yourself, you will be honored." (CEV)

2. _____

　　　　👋　Palms are outward shielding the face; head turned away.

—Luke 11:9—So I say to you, keep asking, and it will be given to you. Keep searching, and you will find. Keep knocking, and the door will be opened to you. (HCSB)

3.　_____

　　　　👋　Hands cupped to receive.

—Luke 22:42—Father, if You are willing, take this cup away from Me—nevertheless, not My will, but Yours, be done. (HCSB)

4.　_____

　　　　👋　Hands folded in prayer and placed high on the forehead to symbolize respect.

Praying Together

How Will God Answer Us?

—Matthew 20:20-22—Then the mother of James and John, the sons of Zebedee, came to Jesus with her sons. She knelt respectfully to ask a favor. "What is your request?" he asked. She replied, "In your Kingdom, please let my two sons sit in places of honor next to you, one on your right and the other on your left." But Jesus answered by saying to them, "You don't know what you are asking! Are you able to drink from the

bitter cup of suffering I am about to drink?" "Oh yes," they replied, "we are able!" (NLT)

1. _____

✋ Shake head signaling "no."

—John 11:11-15—After he had said this, he went on to tell them, "Our friend Lazarus has fallen asleep; but I am going there to wake him up." His disciples replied, "Lord, if he sleeps, he will get better." Jesus had been speaking of his death, but his disciples thought he meant natural sleep. So then he told them plainly, "Lazarus is dead, and for your sake I am glad I was not there, so that you may believe. But let us go to him."

2. _____

✋ Hands push down like slowing a car.

—Luke 9:51-56—As the time drew near for him to ascend to heaven, Jesus resolutely set out for Jerusalem. He sent messengers ahead to a Samaritan village to prepare for his arrival. But the people of the village did not want Jesus to stay there. When James and John saw this, they said to Jesus, "Lord, should we call down fire from heaven to burn them up?" But Jesus turned and rebuked them. So they went on to another village. (NLT)

3. _____

✋ Hands outline a plant growing up.

—John 15:7—But if you remain in me, and my words remain in you, you may ask for anything you want, and it will be granted! (NLT)

4. _____

Head nodding, signaling "yes" and hands moving forward signaling, "go".

Memory Verse

—Luke 11:9—So I say to you, keep asking, and it will be given to you. Keep searching, and you will find. Keep knocking, and the door will be opened to you. (HCSB)

PRACTICE

"The shorter person in the pair will be the leader."

ENDING

God's Phone Number ☙

—Jeremiah 33:3—Call to Me and I will answer you, and I will tell you great and mighty things, which you do not know. (NASB)

Two Hands, Ten Fingers ☙

5

Obey

Obey introduces learners to Jesus as a Servant: servants help people; they have a humble heart, and they obey their master. In the same way Jesus served and followed His Father, we now serve and follow Jesus. As the one with all authority, He has given us four commands to obey: go, make disciples, baptize, and teach them to obey all He has commanded. Jesus also promised that He would always be with us. When Jesus gives a command, we should obey it all of the time, immediately, and from a heart of love.

Storms in life come to everyone, but the wise man builds his life obeying Jesus' commands; the foolish man does not. Finally, learners begin an Acts 29 Map, a picture of their harvest field, which they will present at the end of the Discipleship Seminar.

WORSHIP

PRAYER

1. How can we pray for lost people you know to be saved?
2. How can we pray for the group you are training?

STUDY

Do The Funky Chicken! ☞

Review

What Are Eight Pictures That Help Us Follow Jesus?

Multiply

What are three things a steward does?
What was God's first command to man?
What was Jesus' last command to man?
How can I be fruitful and multiply?
What are the two seas located in Israel?
Why are they so different?
Which one do you want to be like?

Love

What are three things a shepherd does?
What is the most important command to teach others?
Where does love come from?
What is simple worship?
Why do we have simple worship?
How many people does it take to have simple worship?

Pray

What are three things a saint does?
How should we pray?
How will God answer us?
What is God's phone number?

What is Jesus Like?

—Mark 10:45—For even the Son of Man came not to be served, but to serve others, and to give his life as a ransom for many. (NLT)

 Pretend to hammer.

What are Three Things a Servant Does?

—Philippians 2:5-8—Your attitude should be the same as that of Christ Jesus: Who, being in very nature God, did not consider equality with God something to be grasped, but made himself nothing, taking the very nature of a servant, being made in human likeness. And being found in appearance as a man, he humbled himself and became obedient to death—even death on a cross!

1. _____

2. _____

3. _____

Who Has The Highest Authority in the World?

—Matthew 28:18—Then Jesus came to them and said, "All authority in heaven and on earth has been given to me."

What Are Four Commands Jesus Has Given Every Believer?

—Matthew 28:19-20a—Therefore go and make disciples of all nations, baptizing them in the name of the Father and of the Son and of the Holy Spirit, and teaching them to obey everything I have commanded you.

1. _____

🖐 Move fingers forward "walking."

2. _____

🖐 Use all four hand motions from Simple Worship: praise, pray, study, practice.

3. _____

🖐 Put your hand on your other elbow; move the elbow up and down as if someone is being baptized.

4. _____

✋ Put hands together as if you are reading a book, and then move the "book" back and forth from left to right as if you are teaching people.

How Should We Obey Jesus?

1. _____

✋ Move right hand from your left side to right side.

2. _____

✋ Move hands top to bottom in a slicing motion.

3. _____

✋ Cross hands over the chest and then raise hands in praise to God.

What Did Jesus Promise Every Believer?

—Matthew 28:20b—And surely I am with you always, to the very end of the age.

Memory Verse

–John 15:10–When you obey my commandments, you remain in my love, just as I obey my Father's commandments and remain in his love.(NLT)

PRACTICE

"The *tallest person* in the pair will be the leader."

ENDING

Building On the True Foundation ❧

–Mathew 7:24, 25–Anyone who hears and obeys these teachings of mine is like a wise person who built a house on solid rock. Rain poured down, rivers flooded, and winds beat against that house. But it did not fall, because it was built on solid rock. (CEV)

–Matthew 7:26, 27–Anyone who hears my teachings and doesn't obey them is like a foolish person who built a house on sand. The rain poured down, the rivers flooded, and the winds blew and beat against that house. Finally, it fell with a crash. (CEV)

Acts 29 Map - Part 1 ❧

6

Walk

Walk introduces learners to Jesus as a Son: a son/daughter honors his/her father, desires unity, and wants the family to succeed. The Father called Jesus "beloved" and the Holy Spirit descended upon Jesus at His baptism. Jesus was successful in His ministry because He depended on the power of the Holy Spirit.

In the same way, we must depend on the power of the Holy Spirit in our lives. We have four commands to obey concerning the Holy Spirit: walk with the Spirit, do not grieve the Spirit, be filled with the Spirit, and do not quench the Spirit. Jesus is with us today and wants to help us even as He helped people on the roads of Galilee. We can call to Jesus if we need healing from something that is stopping us from following Him.

WORSHIP

PRAYER

1. How can we pray for lost people you know to be saved?
2. How can we pray for the group you are training?

STUDY

Out of Gas ଓ

Review

What Are Eight Pictures That Help Us Follow Jesus?

Multiply

What are three things a steward does?
What was God's first command to man?
What was Jesus' last command to man?
How can I be fruitful and multiply?
What are the two seas located in Israel?
Why are they so different?
Which one do you want to be like?

Love

What are three things a shepherd does?
What is the most important command to teach others?
Where does love come from?
What is simple worship?
Why do we have simple worship?
How many people does it take to have simple worship?

Pray

> *What are three things a saint does?*
> *How should we pray?*
> *How will God answer us?*
> *What is God's phone number?*

Obey

> *What are three things a servant does?*
> *Who has the highest authority?*
> *What are four commands Jesus has given to every believer?*
> *How should we obey Jesus?*
> *What did Jesus promise us?*

What is Jesus Like?

> *—Matthew 3:16, 17—After Jesus was baptized, He went up immediately from the water. The heavens suddenly opened for Him, and He saw the Spirit of God descending like a dove and coming down on Him. And there came a voice from heaven: "This is My beloved Son. I take delight in Him!" (HCSB)*

 Move hands towards mouth as if you are eating. Sons eat a lot!

What are Three Things a Son Does?

> *—John 17:4, 18-21—(Jesus says…) I brought glory to you here on earth by completing the work you gave me to do.*
>
> *Just as you sent me into the world, I am sending them into the world. And I give myself as a holy sacrifice for them so they can*

39

be made holy by your truth. I am praying not only for these disciples but also for all who will ever believe in me through their message. I pray that they will all be one, just as you and I are one—as you are in me, Father, and I am in you. And may they be in us so that the world will believe you sent me. (NLT)

1. _____

2. _____

3. _____

Why Was Jesus' Ministry Successful?

—Luke 4:14—(after His temptation) And Jesus returned to Galilee in the power of the Spirit, and news about Him spread through all the surrounding district. (NASB)

_____

What Did Jesus Promise Believers About the Holy Spirit Before the Cross?

—John 14:16-18—And I will ask the Father, and he will give you another Counselor to be with you forever—the Spirit of truth. The world cannot accept him, because it neither sees him nor knows him. But you know him, for he lives with you and will be in you. I will not leave you as orphans; I will come to you.

1. _____

2. _____

3. _____

4. _____

What Did Jesus Promise Believers About the Holy Spirit After His Resurrection?

—Acts 1:8—But you will receive power when the Holy Spirit comes on you. And you will be my witnesses in Jerusalem, and in all Judea and Samaria, and to the ends of the earth. (NLT)

_____

What Are Four Commands to Obey Concerning the Holy Spirit?

—Galatians 5:16—But I say, walk by the Spirit, and you will not carry out the desire of the flesh. (NASB)

1. _____

✋ "Walk" the fingers on both hands.

—Ephesians 4:30—And don't grieve God's Holy Spirit, who sealed you for the day of redemption. (HCSB)

2. _____

✋ Rub eyes like you are crying then shake head signaling "no."

—Ephesians 5:18—Don't be drunk with wine, because that will ruin your life. Instead, be filled with the Holy Spirit…(NLT)

3. _____

> Make a flowing motion with both hands from your feet to the top of your head.

—I Thessalonians 5:19—Do not quench the Spirit. (NASB)

4. _____

> Do not quench the Spirit.
> Hold right index finger up like a candle. Act as if you are trying to blow it out. Shake your head signaling "no."

Memory Verse

—John 7:38—Anyone who believes in me may come and drink! For the Scriptures declare, "Rivers of living water will flow from his heart." (NLT)

PRACTICE

"The person *who lives the farthest away from the meeting place* in the pair will be the leader."

ENDING

Jesus Is Here ෬

—Hebrews 13:8–Jesus Christ never changes! He is the same yesterday, today, and forever. (CEV)

—Matthew 15:30-31–And large crowds came to Him, bringing with them those who were lame, crippled, blind, mute, and many others, and they laid them down at His feet; and He healed them. So the crowd marveled as they saw the mute speaking, the crippled restored, and the lame walking, and the blind seeing; and they glorified the God of Israel. (NASB)

—John 10:10–The thief comes only to steal and kill and destroy; I have come that they may have life, and have it to the full.

7

Go

Go introduces Jesus as a Seeker: seekers search for new places, lost people, and new opportunities. How did Jesus decide where to go and minister? He did not do it Himself; He looked to see where God was working; He joined God; and He knew that God loved Him and would show Him. How should we decide where to minister?–the same way that Jesus did.

Where is God working? He is working among the poor, captives, sick, and oppressed. Another place God is working is in our families. He wants to save our entire family. Learners locate people and places where God is working on their Acts 29 Map.

WORSHIP

PRAYER

1. How can we pray for lost people you know to be saved?
2. How can we pray for the group you are training?

STUDY

Review

What Are Eight Pictures That Help Us Follow Jesus?

Love

What are three things a shepherd does?
What is the most important command to teach others?
Where does love come from?
What is simple worship?
Why do we have simple worship?
How many people does it take to have simple worship?

Pray

What are three things a saint does?
How should we pray?
How will God answer us?
What is God's phone number?

Obey

What are three things a servant does?
Who has the highest authority?
What are four commands Jesus has given to every believer?

46

How should we obey Jesus?
What is a promise Jesus has given to every believer?

Walk

What are three things a son does?
What was the source of power in Jesus' ministry?
What did Jesus promise believers about the Holy Spirit before the cross?
What did Jesus promise believers about the Holy Spirit after His resurrection?
What are four commands to follow about the Holy Spirit?

What is Jesus Like?

—Luke 19:10—For the Son of Man has come to seek and to save that which was lost. (NASB)

Look back and forth with hand above eyes.

What are Three Things a Seeker Does?

—Mark 1:37, 38—And when they found him, they exclaimed: "Everyone is looking for you!" Jesus replied, "Let us go somewhere else—to the nearby villages—so I can preach there also. That is why I have come."

1. _____

2. _____

3. _____

How Did Jesus Decide Where To Minister?

–John 5:19, 20–Jesus gave them this answer: "I tell you the truth, the Son can do nothing by himself; he can do only what he sees his Father doing, because whatever the Father does the Son also does. For the Father loves the Son and shows him all he does. Yes, to your amazement he will show him even greater things than these."

1. _____

🖐 Put one hand over heart and shake head 'no'.

2. _____

🖐 Put one hand over eyes; search left and right.

3. _____

🖐 Point hand towards a place in front of you and shake head yes.

4. _____

🖐 Raise hands upwards in praise and then cross them over your heart.

How Should We Decide Where To Minister?

—I John 2:5, 6—But those who obey God's word truly show how completely they love him. That is how we know we are living in him. Those who say they live in God should live their lives as Jesus did. (NLT)

How can we know if God is working?

—John 6:44—No one can come to Me unless the Father who sent Me draws him, and I will raise him up on the last day.

Where is Jesus Working?

—Luke 4:18-19—The Spirit of the Lord is upon me, because he anointed me to preach the gospel to the poor. He has sent me to proclaim release to the captives, and recovery of sight to the blind, to set free those who are oppressed, to proclaim the favorable year of the Lord. (NASB)

1. _____

2. _____

3. _____

4. _____

Where is Another Place that Jesus is working?

Demon-Possessed Man–Mark 5

Cornelius–Acts 10

Jailer at Philippi–Acts 16

Memory Verse

> *–John 12:26–Anyone who wants to be my disciple must follow me, because my servants must be where I am. And the Father will honor anyone who serves me. (NLT)*

PRACTICE

"The person *with the most brothers and sisters* in the pair is the leader."

ENDING

ACTS 29 MAP - Part 2 ରେ

"On your Acts 29 Map, draw and label places where Jesus is working. Identify at least five places on your map where you know Jesus is working and draw a cross at each place. Label how God is working in that area."

8

Share

Share introduces Jesus as a Soldier: soldiers fight enemies, endure hardship, and set the captives free. Jesus is a soldier; when we follow Him, we will be soldiers, too.

As soon as we join God where He is working, we encounter spiritual warfare. How do believers defeat Satan? We defeat him by Jesus' death on the cross, sharing our testimony, and not being afraid to die for our faith.

A powerful testimony would be if I share the story of my life before I met Jesus, then how I met Jesus, and the difference that walking with Jesus is making in my life. Testimonies are more effective when we limit our sharing to three or four minutes, when we don't share our conversion age (because age doesn't matter), and when we use language unbelievers can understand easily.

The session ends with a contest: who can most quickly write the names of 40 lost people they know. Prizes are given for first, second, and third place, but ultimately everyone gets a prize because we are all "winners" when we know how to give our testimony.

WORSHIP

PRAYER

1. How can we pray for lost people you know to be saved?
2. How can we pray for the group you are training?

STUDY

Review

What Are Eight Pictures That Help Us Follow Jesus?

Pray

What are three things a saint does?
How should we pray?
How will God answer us?
What is God's phone number?

Obey

What are three things a servant does?
Who has the highest authority?
What are four commands Jesus has given to every believer?
How should we obey Jesus?
What is a promise Jesus has given to every believer?

Walk

What are three things a son does?
What was the source of power in Jesus' ministry?

What did Jesus promise believers about the Holy Spirit before the cross?
What did Jesus promise believers about the Holy Spirit after His resurrection?
What are four commands to follow about the Holy Spirit?

Go

What are three things a seeker does?
How did Jesus decide where to minister?
How should we decide where to minister?
Where is Jesus working?
Where is another place Jesus is working?

What is Jesus Like?

—Matthew 26:53—Don't you know that I could ask my Father, and right away he would send me more than twelve armies of angels? (CEV)

 Raise sword.

What are Three Things a Soldier Does?

—Mark 1:12-15—Right away God's Spirit made Jesus go into the desert. He stayed there for forty days while Satan tested him. Jesus was with the wild animals, but angels took care of him. After John was arrested, Jesus went to Galilee and told the good news that comes from God. He said, "The time has come! God's kingdom will soon be here. Turn back to God and believe the good news!" (CEV)

1. _____

2. _____

3. _____

How Do We Defeat Satan?

—Revelation 12:11—And they have defeated him by the blood of the Lamb and by their testimony. And they did not love their lives so much that they were afraid to die. (NLT)

1. _____

Point to both palms of your hands with your middle finger-the universal sign for crucifixion.

2. _____

Cup hands around mouth as if you are speaking to someone.

3. _____

Place wrists together, as if in chains.

What Is a Powerful Testimony Outline?

1. _____

   👋 Point to the left side in front of you.

2. _____

   👋 Point to the center in front of you.

3. _____

   👋 Turn to your right and move hands up and
   down.

4. _____

   👋 Point to your temple—as if you are thinking about
   a question.

What Are Some Important Guidelines To Follow?

1. _____

2. _____

3. _____

Memory Verse

—1Corinthians 15:3,4—For what I received I passed on to you as of first importance: that Christ died for our sins according to the Scriptures, that he was buried, that he was raised on the third day according to the Scriptures...

PRACTICE

"The *loudest* person will be the leader, the person who goes first."

Salt and Sugar ∞

ENDING

Who Can List Forty Lost People the Fastest? ∞

9

Sow

Sow introduces Jesus as a Sower: sowers plant seeds, tend their fields, and rejoice in a great harvest. Jesus is a Sower and He lives in us; when we follow Him, we will be sowers as well. When we sow a little, we reap a little. When we sow much, we reap much.

What should we sow into people's lives? Only the simple gospel can transform them and bring them back to God's family. Once we know that God is working in a person's life, we share the simple gospel with them. We know it is the power of God to save them.

WORSHIP

PRAYER

1. How can we pray for lost people you know to be saved?
2. How can we pray for the group you are training?

STUDY

Review

What Are Eight Pictures That Help Us Follow Jesus?

Obey

What are three things a servant does?
Who has the highest authority?
What are four commands Jesus has given to every believer?
How should we obey Jesus?
What is a promise Jesus has given to every believer?

Walk

What are three things a son does?
What was the source of power in Jesus' ministry?
What did Jesus promise believers about the Holy Spirit before the cross?
What did Jesus promise believers about the Holy Spirit after His resurrection?
What are four commands to follow about the Holy Spirit?

Go

What are three things a seeker does?
How did Jesus decide where to minister?
How should we decide where to minister?

Where is Jesus working?
Where is another place Jesus is working?

Share

What are three things a soldier does?
How do we overcome Satan?
What is a powerful testimony outline?
What are some important guidelines to follow?

What is Jesus Like?

—Matthew 13:36, 37—Then He (Jesus) left the crowds and went into the house and His disciples came to Him and said, "Explain to us the parable of the tares of the field." And He said, "The one who sows the good seed is the Son of Man..." (NASB)

Sower

 Scatter seed with hand.

What are Three Things a Sower Does?

—Mark 4:26-29—Again Jesus said: God's kingdom is like what happens when a farmer scatters seed in a field. The farmer sleeps at night and is up and around during the day. Yet the seeds keep sprouting and growing, and he does not understand how. It is the ground that makes the seeds sprout and grow into plants that produce grain. Then when harvest season comes and the grain is ripe, the farmer cuts it with a sickle. (CEV)

59

1. _____

2. _____

3. _____

What is the Simple Gospel?

—Luke 24:1-7—On the first day of the week, very early in the morning, the women took the spices they had prepared and went to the tomb. They found the stone rolled away from the tomb, but when they entered, they did not find the body of the Lord Jesus. While they were wondering about this, suddenly two men in clothes that gleamed like lightning stood beside them. In their fright the women bowed down with their faces to the ground, but the men said to them, "Why do you look for the living among the dead? He is not here; he has risen! Remember how he told you, while he was still with you in Galilee: 'The Son of Man must be delivered over to the hands of sinners, be crucified and on the third day be raised again.'"

FIRST...

1. _____

✋ Make a large circle with your hands.

2. _____

✋ Clasp hands together.

SECOND...

1. _____

   Raise fists and pretend to fight.

2. _____

   Clasp hands together and then pull them far apart.

THIRD...

1. _____

   Raise hands above head and make a downward motion.

2. _____

   Put the middle finger of each hand in the palm of the other.

3. _____

   Hold right elbow with left hand and move right arm backward as if being buried.

4. _____

   Raise arm back up with three fingers.

5. _____

✋ Put hands down with palms facing outward. Then, raise your hands and cross your heart.

FOURTH...

1. _____

✋ Raise hands in worship.

2. _____

✋ Palms are outward shielding the face; head turned away.

3. _____

✋ Cup hands.

4. _____

✋ Clasp hands together.

Memory Verse

—Luke 8:15—But the seed on good soil stands for those with a noble and good heart, who hear the word, retain it, and by persevering produce a crop.

PRACTICE

ENDING

Where is Acts 29:21? ଔ

ACTS 29 MAP - Part 3 ଔ

10

Take Up

Take Up is the closing session for the seminar. Jesus gave us the command to take up our cross and follow Him every day. The Acts 29 Map is a picture of the cross that Jesus has called each learner to carry.

In this final session, learners present their Acts 29 Map to the group. After each presentation, the group lays hands on the presenter and Acts 29 Map, praying for God's blessing and anointing on their ministry. The group then challenges the presenter by repeating the command, "Take up your cross, and follow Jesus," three times. Learners present their Acts 29 Map in turn until all have finished. The training time ends with a worship song of commitment to make disciples and a closing prayer by a recognized spiritual leader.

WORSHIP

PRAYER

PRESENTATIONS

Review

What Are Eight Pictures That Help Us Follow Jesus?

Multiply

What are three things a steward does?
What was God's first command to man?
What was Jesus' last command to man?
How can I be fruitful and multiply?
What are the two seas located in Israel?
Why are they so different?
Which one do you want to be like?

Love

What are three things a shepherd does?
What is the most important command to teach others?
Where does love come from?
What is simple worship?
Why do we have simple worship?
How many people does it take to have Simple Worship?

Pray

What are three things a saint does?
How should we pray?
How will God answer us?
What is God's phone number?

66

Obey

What are three things a servant does?
Who has the highest authority?
What are four commands Jesus has given to every believer?
How should we obey Jesus?
What is a promise Jesus has given to every believer?

Walk

What are three things a son does?
What was the source of power in Jesus' ministry?
What did Jesus promise believers about the Holy Spirit before the cross?
What did Jesus promise believers about the Holy Spirit after His resurrection?
What are four commands to follow about the Holy Spirit?

Go

What are three things a seeker does?
How did Jesus decide where to minister?
How should we decide where to minister?
Where is Jesus working?
Where is another place Jesus is working?

Share

What are three things a soldier does?
How do we overcome Satan?
What is a powerful testimony outline?
What are some important guidelines to follow?

Sow

What are three things a sower does?
What is the simple gospel we share?

What Does Jesus Command His Followers To Do Every Day?

—Luke 9:23—Then he said to them all: "If anyone would come after me, he must deny himself and take up his cross daily and follow me."

_____

What Are Four Voices That Call Us To Take Up Our Cross?

THE VOICE ABOVE

—Mark 16:15—And then he told them, "Go into all the world and preach the Good News to everyone." (NLT)

1. _____

🖐 Point finger up towards the sky.

—Luke 16:27-28—"Father," he said, "then I beg you to send him to my father's house—because I have five brothers—to warn them, so they won't also come to this place of torment." (HCSB)

2. _____

🖐 Point finger down toward the ground.

—I Corinthians 9:16—Yet when I preach the gospel, I cannot boast, for I am compelled to preach. Woe to me if I do not preach the gospel!

3. _____

🖐 Point finger towards your heart.

—Acts 16:9—That night Paul had a vision: A man from Macedonia in northern Greece was standing there, pleading with him, "Come over to Macedonia and help us!" (NLT)

4. _____

🖐 Cup hand towards group and make a "come here" motion.

PRAYER

ACTS 29 MAPS ∞

Training Trainers

This section details how to train trainers in a reproducible way. First, we will share with you the outcomes you can reasonably expect after training others with *Making Radical Disciples*. Then, we will outline for you the process of training, which includes 1) worship, 2) prayer, 3) study, and 4) practice, based on the most important commandment. Finally, we share some of the key principles in training trainers we have discovered while training thousands of trainers.

Outcomes

After finishing *Making Radical Disciples*, learners will be able to:

- Teach ten basic discipleship lessons based on Christ to others, using a reproducible training process.
- Recall eight clear pictures that portray a follower of Jesus.
- Lead a simple, small-group worship experience based on the most important commandment.
- Share a powerful testimony and gospel presentation with confidence.
- Present a concrete vision for reaching the lost and training believers using an Acts 29 Map.
- Start a disciple group (some of which will become churches) and train others to do the same.

PROCESS

Each session follows the same format. Listed below is the order and estimated timetable:

PRAISE

- 10 minutes
- Ask someone to open the session, praying for God's blessing and direction for everyone in the group. Enlist someone in the group to lead a few choruses or hymns (depending on your context); an instrument is optional.

PRAYER

- 10 minutes
- Divide learners into pairs with someone they have not been a partner with before. Partners share with each other the answer to two questions:

    1. How can we pray for lost people you know to be saved?
    2. How can we pray for the group you are training?

- If a learner has not started a group, their partner should work with them to develop a list of possible friends and family to train, then pray with the learner for people on their list.

STUDY

The Follow Jesus Training system uses two tracks during the study section based on the simple worship model. The material below explains the first track, which consists of the ten lessons in this manual. The second track runs concurrent to the first track and is composed of lessons based on Bible stories. Turn to page 23 in the section "Simple Worship" for more details concerning the second track.

- 30 minutes
- Each "Study" section starts with "Review." It is a review of the eight pictures of Christ and lessons mastered thus far. By the end of the training, learners will be able to recite the whole training by memory.
- After "Review," the trainer or apprentice trains learners with the current lesson, emphasizing that learners should listen closely because they will be training each other afterwards.
- When trainers present the lesson, they should use the following sequence:

  1. Ask the question.
  2. Read the Scripture.
  3. Encourage learners to answer the question.

This process places the word of God as authority for life and not the teacher. Too often, teachers ask a question, give the answer, and then support their answer with Scripture. That sequence puts the teacher as the authority, rather than the word of God.

- If learners answer the question incorrectly, do not correct them, but ask participants to read the Scripture passage aloud and answer again.
- Each lesson ends with a memory verse. Trainers and learners stand together and recite the memory verse ten times; saying the verse address first, followed by the verse. Learners may use their Bibles or student guides the first six times they say the memory verse. The last four times,

however, the group recites the memory verse from the heart. The entire group recites the verse ten times and then sits down.

PRACTICE

- 30 minutes
- Previously, the trainers divided learners for the "Prayer" segment. Their prayer partner is also their practice partner.
- Each lesson has a method of choosing who the "leader" of the pair will be. The leader is the person who will teach first. The trainer announces the method of choosing the leader of the pair to the group.
- Imitating the trainers, the leader trains their partner. The training period should include the review and the new lesson, and end with the memory verse. Learners stand to recite the "Memory Verse" and sit when it is complete, so trainers can see which learners have finished.
- When the first person in a pair finishes, the second person repeats the process, so they can practice training as well. Ensure that the pair does not skip or take shortcuts in the process.
- Walk around the room while they are practicing to make sure they are following you exactly. Failing to do the hand motions is a dead giveaway that they are not imitating you. Emphasize repeatedly that they should copy you, the trainer.

ENDING

- 20 minutes
- Most sessions end with a practical application learning activity. Give learners plenty of time to work on their Acts

29 Maps and encourage them to walk around and get ideas from others as they work.

- Make any necessary announcements, and then ask someone to pray a blessing on the session. Ask someone who has not prayed before to pray–by the end of the training, everyone should have closed in prayer at least once.

Simple Worship

Simple Worship is a critical component of Follow Jesus Training–one of the key skills for making disciples. Based on the Greatest Commandment, Simple Worship teaches people how to obey the command to love God with all their heart, all of their soul, all of their mind, and all of their strength.

We love God with all of our heart, so we worship Him. We love God with all of our soul, so we pray to Him. We love God with our whole mind, so we study the Bible. Finally, we love God with all our strength, so we practice what we have learned in order to share it with others.

God has blessed small groups all over Southeast Asia who have discovered they can have simple worship anywhere–homes, restaurants, at the park, in Sunday school, even at the Pagoda!

PROCESS

- Divide into groups of four.
- Each person takes a different part of simple worship.
- Each time you practice simple worship, learners rotate which part of simple worship they lead, so by the end of the training time they have done each part at least twice.

Worship

- One person leads the group in singing two choruses or hymns (depending upon your context).
- Instruments are not required.
- In the training session, ask learners to place their chairs as if they are sitting at a café table together.
- Every group will be singing different songs and that is good.
- Explain to the group that this is a time to worship God with all your heart as a group, not to see which group can sing the loudest.

Prayer

- *Another* person (different from the one who led worship) leads the group prayer time.
- The prayer leader asks each of the group members for a prayer request and writes it down.
- The prayer leader commits to pray for these items until the group meets again.
- After each person has shared their prayer request, the prayer leader prays for the group.

Study

- *Another* person in the group of four leads the group study time.
- The study leader tells a story from the Bible in his or her own words; we suggest stories from the Gospels, at least in the beginning.

- Depending on the group, you may ask study leaders to first read the Bible story and then tell it in their own words.
- After the study leader tells the Bible story, they ask their group three questions:

  1. What did this story teach us about God?
  2. What did this story teach us about people?
  3. What did I learn in this story that will help me follow Jesus?

- The group discusses each question together, until the study leader feels the discussion wane; then the leader moves to the next question.

Practice

- *Another* person in the group of four leads the group practice time.
- The practice leader helps the group review the lesson again and insures that everyone understands the lesson and can teach it to others.
- The practice leader tells the same Bible story that the study leader told.
- The practice leader asks the same questions that the study leader asked and the group discusses each question again.

Ending

- The simple worship group ends the time of worship by singing another worship song, or saying the Lord's Prayer together.

Further Study

Consult the following resources for a more in-depth discussion of the topic presented. In new areas of mission work, this is also a good list of first books to translate after the Bible.

Step 1: Grow Strong in the Lord

Bright, Bill (1971). *How to Be Filled with the Holy Spirit.* Campus Crusade for Christ.

Graham, Billy (1978). *The Holy Spirit: Activating God's Power in Your Life.* W Publishing Group.

Patterson, George and Scoggins, Richard (1994).*Church Multiplication Guide.* William Carey Library.

Hybels, Bill (1988). *Too Busy Not to Pray.* Intervarsity Press.

Murray,Andrew (2007). *With Christ in the School of Prayer.* Diggory Press.

Packer, J. I. (1993). *Knowing God.* Intervarsity Press.

Piper, John (2006). *What Jesus Demands from the World.* Crossway Books.

Step 2: Make Disciples

John Chen. *Training For Trainers (T4T)*. Unpublished, no date.

Blackaby, Henry T. and King, Claude V (1990). *Experiencing God: Knowing and Doing the Will of God*. Lifeway Press.

Billheimer, Paul (1975). *Destined for the Throne*. Christian Literature Crusade.

Carlton, R. Bruce (2003). *Acts 29: Practical Training in Facilitating Church-Planting Movements among the Neglected Harvest Fields*. Kairos Press.

Hodges, Herb (2001). *Tally Ho the Fox! The Foundation for Building World-Visionary, World Impacting, Reproducing Disciples*. Spiritual Life Ministries.

Neighbour, Ralph T (1967). *Witness, Take the Stand!* Unknown Binding.

Ogden, Greg (2003). *Transforming Discipleship: Making Disciples a Few at a Time*. Intervarsity Press.

Made in the USA
San Bernardino, CA
06 May 2015